Health and safety in excavations

Be safe and shore

HSG185

HSE BOOKS

© *Crown copyright 1999*
Applications for reproduction should be made in writing to:
Copyright Unit, Her Majesty's Stationery Office,
St Clements House, 2-16 Colegate, Norwich NR3 1BQ

First published 1999

ISBN 0 7176 1563 4

HSG185

This guidance is issued by the Health and Safety Executive.
Following this guidance is not compulsory and you are free to
take other action. But if you do follow this guidance you will
normally be doing enough to comply with the law and may refer
to this guidance as illustrating good practice.

PREFACE

Digging foundations and trenches for drains is one of the first jobs carried out on a construction site, and unhappily for some it is the last that they carry out. Workers with many years experience of excavation work are often deceived by the appearance of ground which they are convinced will stand with little or no support, for as long as they have to work in it. There is almost no ground which can be relied upon to stand unsupported in all circumstances.

Every year too many construction workers are killed and maimed when part of inadequately supported excavations, in which they are working, collapse. The risk is self-evident when you consider that one cubic metre of soil can weigh as much as one tonne, and it is quite common for that volume of soil to collapse into an unsupported excavation.

Never forget that in addition to loss of life, and suffering inflicted on the victim's family, such accidents also cost all involved, whether directly or indirectly, considerable financial loss. A survey carried out by HSE found that accidental loss on a typical construction site cost the contractor 8.5% of the original tender price for the contract.

The aim of this booklet is to help all who are in any way involved in the construction process to identify the main failings in excavation work which lead to physical injury, and financial loss, and to take the necessary measures at the planning stage, to avoid them. That is to say, before any work actually starts on the site.

Reference is also made to other publications which provide guidance on related health and safety issues in excavation work. This booklet is part of HSE's revised series of health and safety guidance for construction.

INTRODUCTION

1 Work in and around any excavation is hazardous. Excavation and groundwork has a poor accident record with an annual average of seven fatal accidents. Table 1 illustrates the type and number of accidents which occur.

Accident description	No of injuries
Struck by flying or falling object, including earth	214
Struck or run over by construction vehicles or plant	141
Falling into an excavation or from plant, materials, ladders or working platforms	128
Contact with electricity	116
Trapped by a collapse of earth, stacked material or plant	100
Other causes	239

Table 1 *Fatal and major injuries to workers engaged in groundwork activities in the period 1991/92 to 1995/96 (excludes minor injuries and accidents involving members of the public).*

2 Many ground types are self-supporting to some extent, but a collapse can occur without warning, resulting in a person being buried, trapped, crushed, or struck by a heavy mass of soil or rock. Never underestimate the risks involved in working in excavations. Over the years, many deaths have occurred in both shallow and deep excavations.

Four very experienced groundworkers were laying foul drains across a greenfield site. The trench was 4.5 m deep and 2.2 m wide, with vertical sides. The contractors were advised to provide shoring but they insisted that the ground, comprising mudstone, was self-supporting and showed no sign of movement. The following day the trench side collapsed catastrophically, killing three of the workers and seriously injuring the fourth.

Introduction

3   Other factors connected with excavation work which have resulted in injuries and deaths include:

(a) people being struck by material from the trench sides, spoil or stored materials falling into excavations;

(b) site vehicles toppling or sliding into excavations, resulting in injury either to excavation workers or vehicle operators;

(c) unfenced excavations into which people have fallen;

(d) contact with underground services, especially gas and electricity;

(e) collapse of structures which have been undermined by poorly supported excavation work.

Who needs to read this book?

4   This guidance should be used by all involved in excavation work including clients, designers, planning supervisors and contractors who have duties under the Construction (Design and Management) Regulations 1994 (CDM).[1] Employers undertaking site work will benefit directly from the practical advice given here, and clients, designers and planning supervisors who study the whole book should improve their understanding of hazards arising from excavation activities. This will help them to achieve fuller compliance with CDM and Construction (Health, Safety and Welfare) Regulations 1996 (CHSW)[2] duties. While primarily of use to managers, supervisors, trades union appointed health and safety representatives and employee representatives, extracts from this guidance should prove useful for inclusion in staff training. Case study summaries of accidents and incidents, brought to the attention of HSE, are provided for use in such contexts and are highlighted as boxed text.

What is covered?

5   The guidance in this booklet concerns construction work such as pipe and cable laying, manhole construction, foundations, small retaining walls and other structures where earthworks are required. It may assist a range of industry sectors, other than construction, where excavation work is undertaken, for example by local authorities (grave digging), in agriculture (land drainage and construction of lagoons), in site investigation work (trial pits), and by archaeologists.

6   The guidance does not extend to the more complex and specialist excavations where significant engineering input is required, such as shaft sinking, heading and tunnelling work, construction of cofferdams and piled support systems and underpinning of structures.

7   Where detailed guidance already exists on topics general to the construction industry, such as transport, protection of the public, avoiding danger from underground and overhead services, this is indicated in the text and the source given in the reference section.

Content

8   The guidance is presented in four main sections:

(a)   **Hazards and control measures** are discussed in detail in the first section. Case studies are used to illustrate the variety of risks which may occur in the course of excavation work. The potential for injury is outlined, along with the steps that can be taken to reduce the likelihood of accidents.

(b)   The **planning, design and management** section contains advice for those involved before excavation work commences on site and includes guidance on site investigation, designing to reduce risk, risk assessment and management issues. Examples are included to illustrate the action that can be taken in such areas.

(c)   The third section lists the main **legal requirements** placed on those involved both directly and indirectly with excavation work.

(d)   The fourth section lists sources of **further information** about managing health and safety risks.

HAZARDS AND CONTROL MEASURES

Trenchless technology

9   These techniques can replace the need for excavation, apart from launch and reception pits. They also reduce risks to members of the public from open excavations and subsequent traffic disruption. The surveying of any obstructions and the control of the cutting head of the machine to avoid them is crucial. Service location plans and location devices should be used to ensure that the route of the bored service does not impinge on existing services (see paragraphs 51-54 and the HSE publication *Avoiding danger from underground services*).[3]

10   Options include:

(a)   *Micro-tunnelling*: a remotely controlled non-man entry pipejacking method using a small diameter full-face tunnel boring machine.

(b)   *Directional drilling*: a method of forming a borehole to a predetermined profile by controlling the direction of a drill head that is launched from the surface or from a pit.

(c)   *Impact moling*: a mole is a pneumatically-operated soil displacement hammer, which is launched from a pit to form a hole through which a service pipe is subsequently pulled. Impact moles cannot be steered and they tend to follow the line of least resistance in the soil so that their line and level have to be fixed to cross existing services at, or near to, a right angle. The use of moles should be avoided in ground crossed by services at a similar depth to the proposed service route.

> *Two 33 kV underground electricity cables were cut by a moling device which was being used for the installation of a water main. The mole was used in an area where there were high voltage electricity cables buried, at the request of the client. Nine thousand people had their electricity supply cut off for two days as a result. Service location plans and location devices were available but not used.*

(d)   *Auger boring*: a technique used to form a lined opening by auger from one pit to another, and is typically used for road crossings, through which other services are subsequently passed.

> *While clearing spoil from the rotating auger of a drilling rig used for horizontal boring, a man became entangled and suffered a fractured arm and dislocated shoulder. An auger cleaner should have been used or the auger should have been stopped while spoil was removed from the flights.*

(e) *Pipe re-lining*: there is a range of techniques used to rehabilitate water mains, sewers, and gas mains. Existing services are either coated internally by a remote method or polyethylene pipes are winched into the existing service. Assessments of exposure to coating products and cleaning agents made in accordance with The Control of Substances Hazardous to Health Regulations 1994 (COSHH)[4] should identify the need for mechanical ventilation and suitable personal protective equipment (PPE).

(f) *Pipe bursting*: impact moles with a bladed cutting edge are used to break existing pipes and new pipes of similar diameter are winched into the resulting space.

Ground movement

11 Excavations in non-cohesive loose sand and gravel, soft clays and silts, will require close sheeting to prevent ground movement. The support must be positioned as soon as possible. The use of sheet piles or trench sheeting driven prior to excavation will be necessary in many cases.

> *In the five-year period between 1991 and 1996, 100 workers were killed or suffered a major injury as a result of being trapped when excavations in which they were working collapsed, adjacent structures were undermined, or stacked materials fell over onto them.*

12 Excavations in cohesive soils and in weak rock may stand unsupported for periods ranging from 30 seconds to 30 days. **But beware**, they are not safe places to work for there is no way of knowing when excavations in ground of this nature will collapse, possibly with fatal consequence. Support is needed to prevent collapse and to ensure the safety of people in and adjacent to the excavation (see Figure 1). Cohesive stiff or very stiff clays may be adequately supported by open or 'hit and miss' trench sheeting where alternate trench sheets are omitted. Care is necessary when excavating rock which may be fractured, to ensure that loose blocks do not fall from the excavated face, especially where bedding planes dip towards the excavation (see Figure 2).

Hazards and control measures

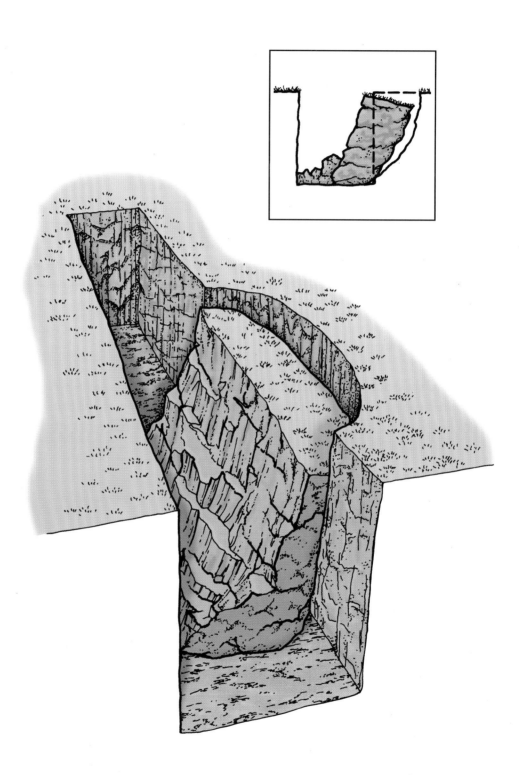

Figure 1   *Slippage of material into trench*

Figure 2   *Risk of material slippage when excavating in fractured rock*

13   People may also be at risk of injury as a result of being struck by falling material if they work close to the base of single-sided excavations, such as those arising during retaining wall construction. People can be trapped between the excavated face and shutters erected for an *in situ* concrete retaining wall. Support should be provided to the excavated face.

> *A carpenter was struck and injured by a large quantity of clay when he entered the area between an excavated face and retaining wall to remove the formwork shutter. The retaining wall was on the boundary of the plot so that it was not possible to batter the excavation side and the scheme design did not allow for raking shores or other methods to achieve support.*

8   Health & safety in excavations

14   Ground type markedly affects the probability, timing, and the extent and nature of collapse. The following factors increase the risk of collapse of excavation sides:

(a)   loose, uncompacted, granular soils, ie sand or gravel, or mixtures containing them;

(b)   excavations through different strata, eg a weak layer lower down in an excavated face can undermine more stable layers above, such as layers of sand or gravel in otherwise stiff clays;

(c)   the presence of groundwater, and the effect on the excavation sides from surface water running into the excavation;

(d)   made-up ground, such as loosely consolidated fill material, old refuse tips, etc;

(e)   proximity to earlier excavations;

(f)   loose blocks of fractured rock;

(g)   weathering, eg rain, drying out, freeze/thaw effects;

(h)   vibration from plant, equipment, road or rail traffic;

(i)   surcharging by spoil, stored materials or plant including vehicles (see paragraphs 16-17);

(j)   proximity of loaded foundations;

(k)   damage to the support system by personnel, or when materials are lowered into the excavation;

(l)   undercutting of the road pavement structure or kerbs and gullies.

A welder died after being struck on the head by a quantity of clay which fell from the side of a 3.1 m deep trench. The clay was dislodged by the passage of an excavator. No shoring had been provided.

15   A competent person needs to frequently assess the ground as excavation proceeds, making allowance for any change in ground conditions.

Surcharging

16   *Surcharging* is the term used to describe any load applied to the ground by plant, stored materials, spoil or structures. Surcharging adjacent to an excavation will increase the horizontal load on the excavation sides. These horizontal loads should be assessed by a competent person and the excavation supports that are installed should be designed to resist them.

17   To reduce the risk of collapse from surcharging, ensure that:

    (a)   spoil from excavations is placed away from the side of an excavation, preferably by a distance of 1.5 m. Where the excavation depth exceeds 1.5 m, this distance needs to equal the depth of the excavation. Boulders need to be pushed into the spoil heap with the excavator bucket;

    (b)   vehicle routes are planned and suitable barriers installed to maintain a safe distance from the excavation edge;

    (c)   temporary support is strengthened where buildings and other structures will create a surcharge, to take account of the additional loading to the ground;

    (d)   additional temporary support is provided for work on sloping sites where there is surcharging on the uphill side of the excavation.

> *A builder was struck and injured by a quantity of earth which fell from the side wall of a 1.4 m deep excavation cut into a small bank. The bank rose 600 mm above general ground level and acted as a natural surcharge.*

Ground and surface water

18   Depending on the permeability of the ground, water may flow into any excavation below the natural groundwater level. The supports to the side of the excavation should be designed to control the entry of groundwater and the design of support works should take any additional hydrostatic loading into account. Particular attention should be given to areas close to rivers, lakes and sea.

19   Water entering the excavation needs to be channelled to sumps from where it can be pumped out; however, the effect of pumping from sumps on the stability of the excavation should be considered.

20   In sandy or silty ground where the permeability is high, de-watering techniques such as well pointing, or deep wells, should be considered. These techniques are used locally to depress the water table to a level below the base of the excavation. Continuous pumping is expensive and continual flow from the surrounding ground may cause ground settlement which could adversely affect adjacent buildings or services. Designers will need to consider these issues.

21   In ground where de-watering techniques may not be appropriate, other methods of controlling the flow of groundwater could be considered. Such methods include ground freezing and providing an impermeable barrier by injecting grouts to fill

the pore spaces, fissures or cavities close to the excavation. The grout can be cement, bentonite or chemical. These methods are expensive and their effectiveness cannot be guaranteed. Pumping grout under pressure can cause disruption and displacement of the ground and it can travel some distance along permeable layers or planes of weakness. The consequences of grout failure need to be taken into account in the risk assessment.

22   The designer should ensure that any upward flow of water is not sufficient to produce 'piping' or 'boiling' at the base of an excavation whereby the soil cannot support any vertical load; this can result in risk of injury to people in the excavation as well as a threat to its overall stability.

23   Advice should be sought from the Environment Agency on the disposal of dirty or contaminated groundwater.

Stability of adjacent structures and services

24   Whenever an excavation is to be carried out close to services or existing buildings or structures, including earthworks such as railway embankments, care should be taken to ensure that the services or foundations of such buildings or structures are not disturbed or undermined (see Figures 3 and 4).

> *A labourer suffered multiple fractures to his head and upper body when a 1.2 m brick garden wall, situated immediately next to the trench he was excavating, collapsed. The trench was no more than 900 mm in depth but the garden wall had very shallow foundations and had been completely undermined.*

25   In all types of soil, some inward movement of the sides of an excavation will occur. Any lateral movement will produce settlement of the surrounding ground, the amount depending on the type of ground and the care taken with the installation of the support. For excavations in rock, movement along bedding planes may have to be considered (see Figure 2).

26   Settlement may be sufficient to damage adjacent buildings and services. Building foundations that are at a distance of less than two times the excavation depth from the face of the excavation are more likely to be affected by ground movement; underpinning of such structures may be necessary to prevent structural damage.

27   Further settlement will occur if excavations are not backfilled adequately. Backfill needs to be placed and compacted in layers and all spaces, including those created when temporary supports are removed, need to be filled. Temporary supports should not be withdrawn until sufficient backfill has been placed to prevent the excavation from collapsing.

28   Retaining walls rely on the passive resistance of the ground at the front of the wall to prevent them sliding and rotating. Any reduction of this resistance will adversely affect the stability of the wall. Excavations in ground which is providing passive resistance to a structure such as at the toe of a retaining wall should not begin before being assessed by a competent engineer.

Figure 3   *Undermining of boundary wall*

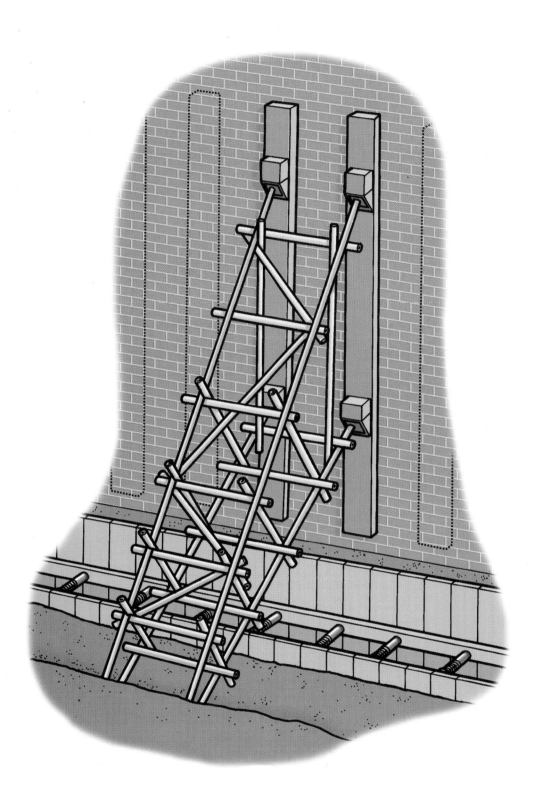

Figure 4   *Shoring of building with excavation at base*

Battering and stepping

29   Any unsupported excavation will be safe without support *only* if its sides are battered back sufficiently, or if the excavation is in sound rock. Battering back the sides of an excavation to a safe angle is an acceptable means of preventing instability. In many situations this is the simplest and safest way of ensuring stability and should receive first consideration. In granular soils the angle of slope should be less than the natural angle of repose of the material being excavated. In wet ground a considerably flatter slope will be required.

30   Typical slope angles are shown in the Table 2 and Figure 5.

Table 2 Typical safe slope angles (in degrees to the horizontal) for battering back sides of an excavation

Material	Dry ground	Wet ground
Gravel	30-40°	10-30°
Sand	30-35°	10-30°
Silt	20-40°	5-20°
Clay	20-45°	10-35°
Peat	10-45°	5-35°

31   Care needs to be taken in the use of the figures in Table 2 as soils in their natural state are often a combination of those listed. A small percentage increase in the water content of some soils can also significantly reduce their natural strength. Battered excavations require regular monitoring. Regular scaling of rock excavations may be necessary.

32   Stepping the excavation sides is an alternative to battering. In this method one or more steps are cut into the excavation side(s). The depth and width of the step need to be determined using the typical slope angles given in Table 2, although the vertical distance should not exceed 1.2 m.

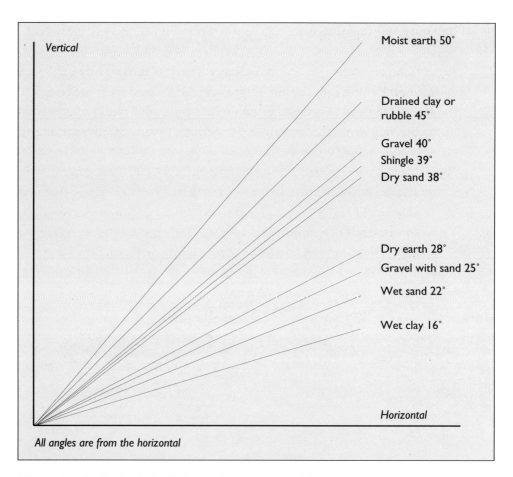

Vertical

Moist earth 50°

Drained clay or rubble 45°

Gravel 40°
Shingle 39°
Dry sand 38°

Dry earth 28°
Gravel with sand 25°
Wet sand 22°

Wet clay 16°

Horizontal

All angles are from the horizontal

Figure 5   *Graph of typical safe slope angles, see paragraph 31*

Methods of ground support

Proprietary systems

33   The use of proprietary ground support systems offers advantages over traditional systems. Such advantages include:

(a)   the ease and improved safety of installation: operatives can install most proprietary ground support systems without the need to enter the excavation;

(b)   systems are available to suit a wide range of applications;

(c)   increased working space for ease of excavation and pipe laying;

(d)   the availability of technical advice on selection, installation and use.

34   Proprietary ground support equipment always needs to be installed, removed and stored when not in use in accordance with the manufacturer's instructions.

35   The following types of proprietary ground support equipment are available:

(a)   *Hydraulic waling frames* comprise two steel or aluminium beams braced apart by struts containing integral hydraulic rams. They can be used for close or open sheeting applications in trenches and for supporting close sheeting in deep excavations for which frames at various levels may be required (see Figure 6).

(b)   *Manhole shores* are four-sided adjustable frames with integral hydraulic rams and are intended for supporting excavations for manholes, foundations, small tanks and pits and similar structures. Waling frames and manhole shores should be supplied complete with chains or other means by which they can be hung from the sheeting or from other frames (see Figure 7).

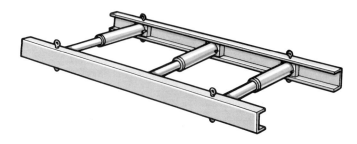

Figure 6   *Hydraulic waling frame*

Figure 7   *Manhole shore*

(c)   *Trench boxes* consist of modular side panels strutted apart by adjustable struts to suit the width of trench. Their height can be increased by the addition of extension panels. The location of the struts is variable within limits, depending on the ground clearance required. The lower edges of the side panels are tapered to form a cutting edge (see Figure 8). Boxes should be progressively dug in as the excavation work proceeds, or they can be lowered by an excavator or crane into a pre-dug trench. Where more than one box is required due to the depth, the boxes should either remain connected if lowered into a pre-dug trench or be connected/disconnected at ground level by progressive excavation/backfilling. Install sufficient boxes so that the full depth of the excavation is supported before people enter the excavation. If the excavation is overdug, backfill needs to be placed between the excavation side and the box to prevent both the risk of people falling into the gap and of rotation of the box following ground movement. If required, trench sheets should be positioned at the open ends to prevent material falling inwards. Some configurations of box may be unstable when standing upright on the surface and should be either laid flat or 'dug in'.

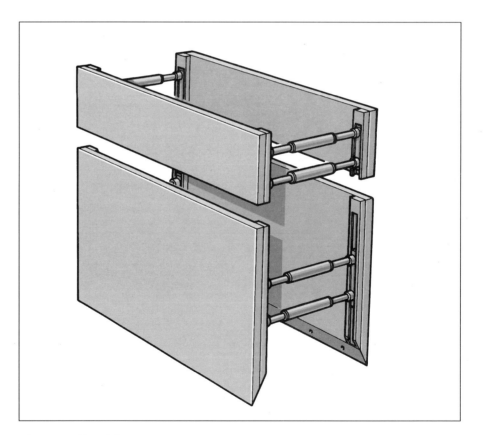

Figure 8   *Trench box*

A pipelayer was struck by falling clay while he assisted in the removal of a trench box. Trenches had been excavated which were 4 m deep and supported using a combination of base unit (2.5 m) and top unit (1.5 m) trench boxes. As a result of limited lifting capacity, the two units were being installed and removed sequentially in trenches dug to full depth. To connect and disconnect lifting chains to the bottom box, employees had to enter trenches where the upper 1.5 m was not supported.

(d)   *Drag boxes* comprise two flat-bottomed side panels with tapered cutting edges to their leading ends. They are braced apart by tubular struts, the leading strut being specially strengthened to allow for the dragging of the box by the excavator. As the box is dragged forwards the excavation behind it is left open (see Figure 9).

Figure 9   *Drag box*

A trench 3.5 m deep had been excavated for pipe laying. A drag box had been inserted which supported the upper 2.5 m only. Material fell into the excavation from the unsupported part and trapped the pipelayer against a pipe, fracturing his leg.

Hazards and control measures

(e)   *Slide-rail systems* comprise vertical slide rails strutted apart by adjustable tubular struts with modular side panels for ground support located in the rails. The rails are usually long enough to hold two or three side panels in a stack. Slide-rail systems provide continuous protection and are suitable for poor ground conditions and deep excavations. They are suited to greenfield sites but lack the flexibility to deal with service crossings within an excavation. They provide protection for the workers within them but do not prevent ground movement behind the side panels. Additional support may be required at stop ends (see Figure 10).

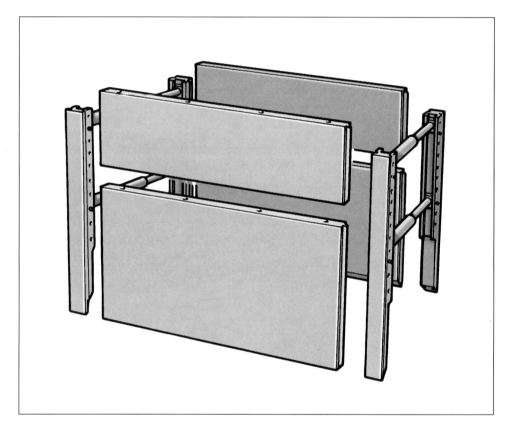

Figure 10   *Slide-rail system*

36   The use of all box systems is limited to locations which are free of buried obstructions. Boxes provide protection to people working inside them but they do not prevent ground movement as they do not necessarily provide support to excavations.

37   The use of lightweight piling frames is not within the scope of this document.

Safe use of proprietary systems

38   When using proprietary ground support systems always:

(a)   ensure that workers stay inside the protected area;

(b)   obtain and follow the manufacturer's instructions for installation and use;

(c)   train and supervise the people who will use the equipment;

(d)   use the correct tools for connecting and disconnecting hydraulic hoses and releasing hydraulic pressure in the rams;

(e)   inspect the equipment before taking it into use;

(f)   ensure all hydraulic components are pressurised to the manufacturer's recommended working pressure;

(g)   ensure that the supporting chains or slings are properly used;

(h)   use additional equipment if required for stop-end protection;

(i)   regularly inspect the installation and in particular its hydraulic system, if any, and carry out remedial or maintenance work to the system in use;

(j)   take care that equipment is not damaged by plant or by rough handling and replace any that is damaged, using only parts that are approved by the manufacturer;

(k)   clean, inspect and maintain the equipment following use and store in a stable manner.

Special applications

39   A large area of clear working space is required for the installation at filling stations of underground tanks for the storage of petroleum spirit. A heavy duty hydraulic waling frame, comprising large section steel beams braced apart by large-capacity hydraulic jacks, has been developed for this application.

40   A scheme of raking shores, steel sheeting and walings can be used to provide support to single-sided excavations. Such schemes need specialist design input by competent engineers.

41   Single-sided excavations in rock may not require support but precautions are normally necessary to prevent loose material falling onto anyone working at the base. In these instances, geotextiles or sprayed concrete may be necessary in addition to the scaling-down of the face to remove loose, significantly sized material.

42   A proprietary lightweight coffin-shaped box system is available for use in cemeteries.

Traditional ground support and its safe installation

43   This is either in the form of timber boards supported by timber walings and struts or by steel trench sheeting or sheet piling supported by timber or steel walings and struts (see Figures 11 and 12).

> *An experienced groundworker was buried in sand up to his neck as he worked in a 2.2 m deep trench. The trench had been excavated between the stone wall of a church and a busy high street to install drainage. The ground consisted of stiff sand with small boulders. Trench sheets had been positioned at 900 mm centres and propped directly back onto the church wall. No walings were used. As a heavy breaker was used to remove boulders, the shoring gave way and the ground collapsed completely.*

Figure 11   *Trench sheets with timber walings, screw props, puncheons and sole plates*

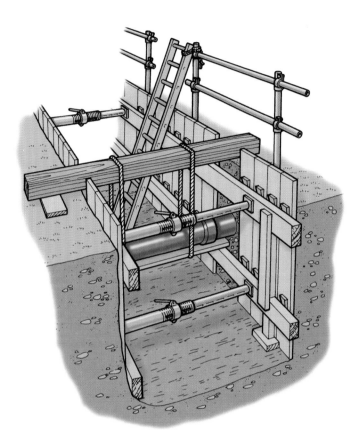

Figure 12   *Timbered excavation with ladder access and supported services (guard rails omitted from left hand side for clarity)*

Open sheeting

44   A common safe sequence of work (see Figure 13) is as follows:

(a)   excavate to depth a section of trench the length of a waling;

(b)   place vertical trench sheets at each end of the trench and drive them into the base of the excavation with the excavator bucket;

(c)   install a horizontal waling along each side of the excavation about 300 mm below ground level by hanging it from the top of the trench sheets;

(d)   working from a lightweight staging (with guard rails affixed) laid across the trench, insert a strut between the walings at the location of the trench sheets;

(e)   install the sheets between the walings and the trench sides and drive into the base of the excavation;

(f)   install intermediate struts as necessary from the lightweight staging (and install edge protection as necessary to prevent people falling into the trench);

(g)   position a ladder into the excavation, secure, and install lower and intermediate walings as required by the design.

Alternatively, hydraulic waling frames which can be inserted from ground level may be used following steps (c)-(g).

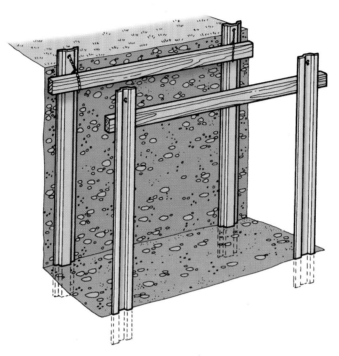

Figure 13 (a)   *Safe installation of traditional support as outlined in paragraphs 44(a-c). Insertion of two pairs of trench sheets and installation of walings hung from trench sheets*

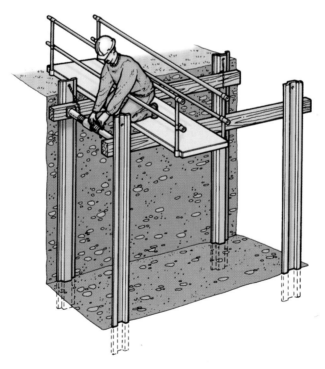

Figure 13 (b)   *Insertion of an adjustable strut between walings working from a staging spanning the trench, as described in paragraph 44(d)*

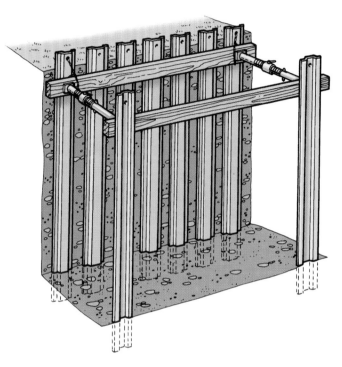

Figure 13 (c)   *Insertion and toeing-in of the remainder of the trench sheets, as outlined in paragraph 44(e)*

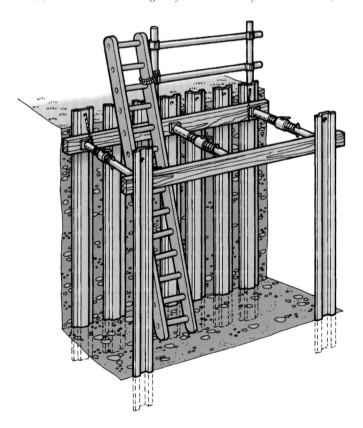

Figure 13 (d)   *Installation of edge protection and a tied ladder, as described in paragraph*
44(f and g). Trench sheets on near side of trench omitted for clarity

Close sheeting

45   A safe sequence of work is as follows:

(a)   excavate a section of trench the length of a waling but only deep enough to install the top waling;

(b)   place vertical trench sheets at each end of the trench and drive them into the base of the excavation with the excavator bucket;

(c)   install a horizontal waling along each side of the excavation about 300 mm below ground level by hanging it from a trench sheet laid on the ground;

(d)   working from a lightweight staging (with guard rails affixed) laid across the trench, insert a strut between the walings at the location of the trench sheets;

(e)   install the sheets between the walings and the trench sides and drive into the base of the excavation;

(f)   install intermediate struts as necessary from the lightweight staging between the upper waling;

(g)   excavate the trench to the level of the next waling frame, driving the sheets into the base of the excavation;

(h)   install the waling frame and intermediate struts by hanging from the one above;

(i)   repeat steps (g) and (h) as necessary until all waling frames are installed.

Alternatively, hydraulic waling frames which can be inserted from ground level may be used, following steps (c)-(i).

46   Installation of ground support is skilled work which should only be undertaken by those with sufficient training and experience, working under the supervision of a competent person.

Further considerations for safe use of traditional support

47   These are as follows:

(a)   support underground services which are exposed by the excavation (see Figure 12), but do not use them to support other services, walings, etc;

(b)   support ground below the services by cross poling and remember that ground above the service may not be as well compacted as that to the side of it;

(c)   toe-in all timber boards, trench sheeting and sheet piling by driving down to an adequate depth beneath the base level of the excavation, unless there is adequate support by alternative means;

(d)   provide additional struts and walings at changes in cross-section and at
stop-ends;

(e)   support and secure all walings and struts using chains hung from the top
of the sheeting, prop from below with puncheons, or otherwise support to
resist displacement by forces from any direction;

(f)   obtain technical specifications for adjustable trench struts from the
manufacturer or supplier when designing support systems and install in
accordance with the instructions supplied. Adjustable steel props designed
for use in falsework support ought not to be used;

(g)   load trench struts axially and ensure that the ends are supported. Timber
packing should be used to prevent struts bearing directly on steel;

(h)   allow for safe dismantling when planning and constructing the ground
support works by using adjustable trench struts rather than solid timber
struts and wedges in timbered support systems.

48   In deep trenches and/or poor ground it may be necessary to drive the sheeting or
piling ahead of excavation. As excavation proceeds, support for the sheeting or
piling should be erected by people working from within areas of sheeting or piling
which have already been supported.

Underpinning

49   Excavation for the purpose of underpinning buildings or structures needs to be
carried out in accordance with the guidance in this booklet. The additional risk
of collapse of the overhead structure should be assessed. As a result of space
constraints, support will often have to consist of timbering to suit the size of
excavation, although there is some scope for the use of hydraulic supports.

50   Detailed guidance on underpinning techniques is beyond the scope of this
guidance.

Underground services

51   Many serious accidents have occurred when buried services have been damaged
during excavation work.

*An average of 23 groundworkers are seriously injured each year through
contact with live electrical systems.*

In particular, contact with any electricity cables can result in explosion and burns to those in the vicinity.

> *A man working in a town centre location lost both his arms when he struck a buried 11 kV cable with a pneumatic breaker at 0.5 m deep. The existence of the cable was known and the excavation was within 0.5 m of its estimated position. No trial holes had been dug using hand tools.*

52   Escaping gas which ignites can cause serious injury and/or property damage as a result of fire and explosion. Serious incidents have arisen where gas from damaged pipes has tracked back underground into buildings where it has subsequently ignited.

53   Excavation should not commence until all available service location drawings have been examined. These should not be considered as completely accurate and serve only to indicate the likely presence of services. It is therefore essential that service-locating devices are used by properly trained people to identify as far as possible the actual location of underground services. Safe digging practice should then be observed which involves the use of hand tools when in the vicinity of underground services. Further advice on this matter is contained in the publication *Avoiding danger from underground services.*[3]

54   Where services cross the line of the trench, they need to be properly supported to prevent damage.

Overhead lines

55   Burns and electrocution can result if raised tipper truck bodies, cranes or excavators touch or come close enough to overhead power lines to cause arcing. There is a risk to all those close to the item of plant which becomes live, as well as to the operator. The need to undertake excavation work close to or below such lines should be very carefully considered and avoided where possible. Highly visible barriers should be erected at least 6 m away from overhead lines to prevent inadvertent approach to them. Crossing points beneath the lines need to be clearly defined by means of red and white goalpost arrangements and signs (see Figures 14(a) and (b)).

Figure 14 (a)   *Precautions for overhead lines: 'goal post' crossing points beneath lines to avoid contact by plant*

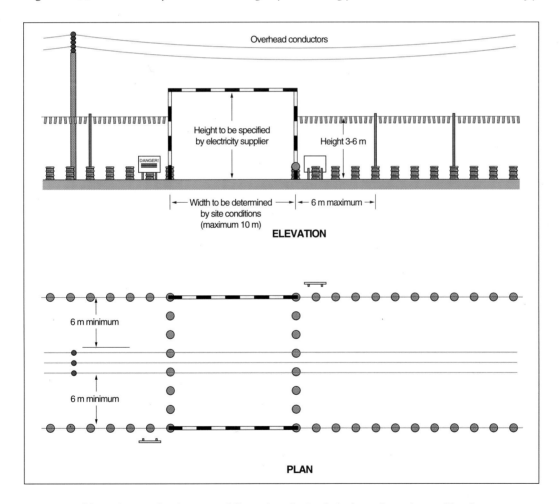

Figure 14 (b)   *Diagram showing normal dimensions for 'goal post' crossing points and barriers*

56   Where work has to be undertaken close by or beneath overhead lines, enquiries should be made with the line operator by the planning supervisor at an early stage to establish whether the line can be made dead or be diverted. The results of such enquiries may influence the scheme design and/or working methods and should be recorded in the pre-tender health and safety plan. Where lines will remain live, plant should be selected or modified so that it cannot reach the lines. Consideration should also be given to avoiding the use of conductive materials such as scaffold tubes for edge protection or aluminium ladders for access.

57   Further guidance is contained in the publication guidance note *Avoidance of danger from overhead electric lines*.[5] Advice should *always* be sought from the local electricity supplier or the railway infrastructure controller, as appropriate.

Falls into excavations

People

58   The top of an excavation presents a fall risk to people close by. All excavations more than 2 m deep should be provided with suitable barriers, *usually* comprising guard and intermediate rails and toeboards. Guard-rail assemblies can be fabricated which either connect to trench box sides and can be easily lifted on and off, or which can be inserted into the ground immediately next to the supported excavation side (see Figure 15).

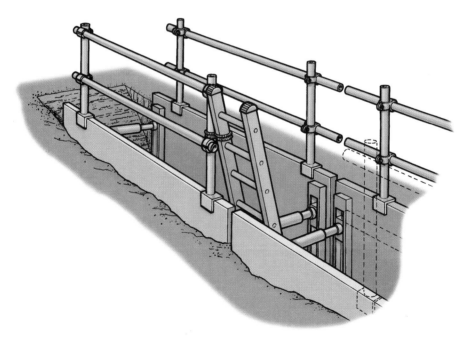

Figure 15   *Trench box with guard rails attached*

59   Where there is a fall risk of less than 2 m but an additional hazard caused, for example, by standing water or by reinforcing bars projecting upwards, the same standard of fall protection should be provided.

> *In the five-year period between 1991 and 96, 143 people, including members of the public, were killed or suffered major injury as a result of falling into excavations.*

60   Edge protection can be achieved in alternative ways if use is made of the support system itself, for example using trench box extensions or trench sheets longer than the trench depth. Where close sheeting is not required, a timber board should be set just into the ground at the rear of the trench sheets to act as a toeboard and to prevent loose material falling into the excavation.

61   It needs to be remembered that edge protection is required to prevent risk to everyone on site, including workers actually involved with excavation work, such as those directing vehicles and lifting appliances, and those passing plant and materials in and out of the excavation.

> *A worker sustained back injuries when he fell 3.6 m into an excavation provided with trench sheeting. Two-metre high panels of weld mesh fencing had been placed around the excavation to keep trades other than ground workers away from it but these had been partially removed to allow the passage of an excavator. After ascending the ladder access, the worker tripped over a cable near the excavation edge and fell. The fencing provided was not adequate to prevent the risk of the groundworkers falling.*

62   Jumping or stepping over a trench can be dangerous. Where necessary access-ways of at least 600 mm width, with edge protection, should be provided (see Figure 16). The need to cross trenches can be reduced by limiting the length of trench left open.

> *An elderly member of the public suffered a fractured skull when he fell into a 2.5 m deep trench excavated in a main road. No barrier had been placed around the trench.*

Figure 16 *Access-way across trench*

63   Where excavations are necessary in areas normally accessible to the public, precautions are required to ensure public safety, particularly of children, and those with impaired mobility or sight. Barriers provided should be constructed to the standard outlined in paragraph 58.[6]

64   As a minimum, signing and barriers complying with Department of Transport guidance[7] should be provided at road and street works. Fencing or hoarding may be required where it is necessary to prevent unauthorised access to a site as a whole or where factors such as volume of pedestrian traffic or depth of excavation are apparent. Risk assessment should determine the measures necessary (see Figure 17).

65   Consideration needs to be given to tripping hazards resulting from damage to the permanent surface, poor reinstatement, stored materials, trailing hoses or cables and temporary pipework. Where temporary covers are provided, they should be of good condition, substantial enough to provide sufficient support and prevent displacement, and should not in themselves present a tripping hazard. Proprietary covers with chamfered edges are available. Contractors should ensure that excavations in footways are left in a safe condition, or properly reinstated, at the end of each working day.

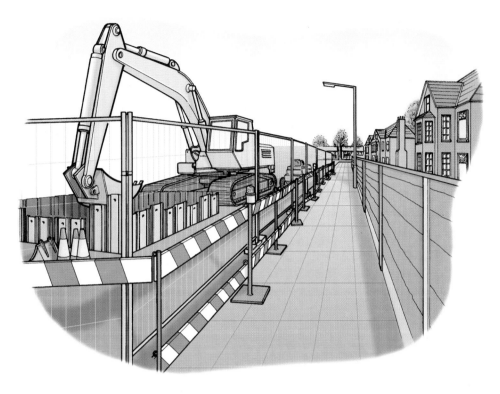

Figure 17   *Barriers around excavation in footway*

Entry and exit

66   A safe means to enter and exit an excavation should be provided.[8] Serious injuries
       have occurred when workers have fallen from props that form part of the ground
       support when these have been used to climb in and out of the excavation. This
       practice also carries risk of disturbance to, and weakening of, the support.

> *Two workers were injured when they fell 3.9 m to the bottom of a fully
> timbered 4.9 m deep telecommunications manhole. Both had stood on a single
> strut to measure for a concrete delivery chute. The strut was held between
> walings merely by pieces of 50 mm x 25 mm timber nailed onto the top
> surface of the strut. The weight of both workers on the strut at the same time
> caused the nails fixing the securing timber to pull out.*

67   Ladders should be positioned within the excavation at a height:base ratio not
       flatter than 4:1 and secured by tying at the upper end to prevent slipping. The
       upper end of the ladder should project at least 1 m above ground level to ensure
       sufficient hand hold. Ladders should be positioned where they will not be
       damaged by plant or from materials-handling operations.

A young engineer was injured when she was asked to check the level of the top of a manhole chamber. She jumped from ground level onto the top of the chamber, slipped and fell 2.7 m into the excavation.

68   The provision of a good standard of access is also important for emergency use should it be necessary to vacate an excavation quickly due to flooding, build-up of fumes, etc. Emergency arrangements need to address how an injured person, unable to use a ladder access, will be recovered.

Plant

69   Heavy plant toppling into an excavation can cause serious injury to those working within it and to the plant operator.

In the five-year period between 1991 and 1996, 141 workers suffered major injury or were killed in transport-related accidents during groundwork.

70   Vehicle routes should be carefully planned so that plant does not have to approach close to the edge of an excavation.[9] These routes need to be clearly marked, for instance with baulks of timber and/or fencing. If plant, such as dumpers or excavators, is used to tip material into an excavation, properly secured stop blocks should be provided to prevent accidental overrunning (see Figures 18 and 19).

71   If shallow excavations have not been shored, plant positioned close to the edge may result in collapse, causing the plant to move unexpectedly and injuring the operator or others close by. Use of plant in this way should either be avoided or trench support provided, however shallow the excavation.

A groundworker was injured while backfilling an 850 mm depth trench with pea gravel in which a 150 mm pipe had already been laid. A backhoe loader was being used to place the pea gravel, directed by a groundworker standing just to the right-hand edge of the machine. After the load was released, one of the machine's front wheels slipped into the trench as the side gave way and in doing so trapped the groundworker against the other side of the trench. No stop blocks or temporary support had been provided and the ground - worker was standing in an unsafe position.

Figure 18   *Vehicle protection at top of an excavation*

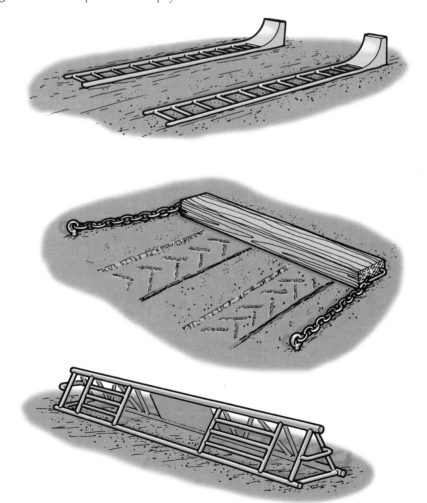

Figure 19   *Stop blocks for dumpers*

72   Workers should *never* remain in a trench or other excavation when they are in the vicinity of materials being deposited into the trench by plant.

Materials

73   Workers will be at risk of injury from spoil or stored materials falling into excavations from the surface unless careful control is exercised. Spoil, equipment and materials should be positioned away from the excavation edge (see *Surcharging*, paragraphs 16-17) and any edge protection should include toeboards or other means such as projecting trench sheet or box sides. Head protection should be worn.

Lifting plant

74   Many items of ground support equipment and drainage/pipework materials are beyond the lifting capabilities of workers. In these cases manual handling assessments,[10-12] will identify the need for slinging and mechanised lifting. The use of mechanical plant reduces the risk of injury from manual handling, but cranes and other lifting equipment can create other hazards in relation to surcharging (paragraphs 16-17) and overhead lines (paragraphs 55-57). Lifting operations are potentially high risk, and demand high safety standards.

75   Contractors need to:

   (a)   select suitable lifting plant, taking account of ground conditions and the loads/radius anticipated;
   (b)   position lifting equipment to avoid imposing undue additional loading on the ground immediately adjacent to the excavation;
   (c)   ensure that each large item of ground support equipment, such as a box, is clearly marked with its self-weight;
   (d)   ensure lifting operations are properly planned, supervised, and carried out.

Inhalation of toxic gas and oxygen deficiency

76   The application of the Confined Spaces Regulations 1997 should be considered for work within excavations, manholes and inspection chambers.[13]

77   Consideration should be given to the potential presence, within excavations, of fumes which can cause asphyxiation and/or poisoning. The products of combustion can seep into and collect within trenches if petrol or diesel engine equipment is sited close to the top. (Such equipment should never be taken into an

excavation.) Ground such as chalk or limestone in contact with acidic groundwater can liberate carbon dioxide. Glauconitic sand (eg Thanet sand) can oxidise, causing oxygen deficiency. Gases such as methane or hydrogen sulphide can seep into excavations from contaminated ground or damaged services in built-up areas. Further guidance on work in contaminated ground can be found in HSE's publication *Protection of workers and the general public during the development of contaminated land.*[14]

> *Three workers died from asphyxiation when the manhole they were working in became contaminated with hydrogen sulphide. Initially, only one was affected, then another entered to render assistance. The third worker died when he went to the aid of the first two. The manhole had been connected to a live sewer on the previous day.*

78   The assessment carried out before work commences needs to identify the risk of toxic gas, oxygen deficiency, and fire or explosion. It should also identify the appropriate risk control measures required, such as:

(a)   type of gas monitoring equipment to be provided;
(b)   testing of the atmosphere before entry into the excavation;
(c)   provision of suitable ventilation equipment;
(d)   training of employees;
(e)   use of a sufficient number of people including one at ground level;
(f)   procedures and equipment needed for an emergency rescue.

Common health hazards

79   Groundworkers can be exposed to numerous health hazards. Guidance is provided in *Protection of workers and the general public during the development of contaminated land, A step-by-step guide to COSHH assessments* and *Health risk management.*[14-16] Exposure will vary and assessments should be made to determine which controls may be necessary.[4]

Micro-organisms

80   Excavation work can bring operatives into contact with ground contaminated by harmful organisms and it should be remembered that the Control of Substances Hazardous to Health Regulations 1994[4] apply equally to micro-organisms as to chemical contaminants. Work near lakes, rivers, sewers and other standing water will expose contractors to the risk of contracting leptospirosis (Weil's disease).

Where a leptospirosis risk can be anticipated, all workers should be advised of the symptoms and provided with medical contact cards to be presented to medical staff if they become ill. Any open cuts should be covered with a waterproof plaster.[17]

81   Sewage is commonly encountered either in ground contaminated by damaged drains or when new pipework is connected to an existing sewer.[18,19] This can result in gastro-enteritis or, less commonly, hepatitis A. An inoculation is available to reduce the risk of contracting hepatitis A. Suitable personal protective equipment (PPE) such as waterproof/abrasion-resistant gloves, footwear, eye and respiratory protection should be provided.

82   All construction workers are at risk of contracting tetanus. If an individual suffers a penetrating dirty wound, medical advice should be sought to arrange for a possible booster injection.

Chemical contaminants

83   Health risks can arise through contact with ground contaminated during previous industrial use or landfill.[14] Excavations near the site of current or former industrial processes such as chemical works, gas works, steel works or foundries and domestic or industrial waste tips and landfill areas are likely to be in contaminated ground which could contain, for example, asbestos, coal-tar residues, lead alkyls or mercurial compounds.

84   The pre-tender health and safety plan needs to detail the hazards likely to be encountered as identified during site investigation and soil sampling. The principal contractor's construction phase plan should describe how the risks will be dealt with. Contaminated material should be removed from site to a disposal facility licensed by the Environment Agency.[20]

85   COSHH assessments should identify risks arising from contact with contaminated soils and any precautions that will be necessary. Where possible, work methods should be modified to reduce contact with contaminated material but if risk remains, appropriate PPE should be provided. Workers should be informed of the possible health effects and how to use the PPE effectively.[21-28]

86   A high standard of personal hygiene is essential where there is exposure to either micro-organisms or chemical contaminants and the necessary washing and eating facilities should be available at the site.[29,30]

Noise and vibration

87   The use of pneumatic breakers over even short periods carries serious risk of both noise-induced hearing loss[31-34] and hand-arm vibration syndrome[35,36] including vibration white finger. Consideration needs to be given at the planning stage to alternative excavation methods.

88   Noise and vibration levels generated by pneumatic breakers in excavation work have regularly been found to exceed 110 dB(A) and 25 m/s^2. The action level for each being 90 dB(A) and 2.8 m/s^2 respectively.

89   Where breakers have to be used, assessment should be made of noise and vibration exposure. A good starting-point is to obtain information from machine suppliers on likely exposure levels. The assessment should identify who is exposed and for how long, followed by a comparison with the current exposure standards. An action plan should then be formulated, detailing steps to reduce exposure and to train and instruct employees.

90   To minimise risk of hearing damage, all tools and equipment need to be well-maintained. Noise levels should be reduced at source as far as possible and in this context avoidable noise exposure caused by poorly sited or unenclosed compressors, breakers without mufflers, and air leaks need to be kept to a minimum. Ear protection which provides a minimum of 25 dB(A) attenuation will normally be necessary for all workers exposed and this should be compatible with other PPE such as head and eye protection.

91   To reduce risk of effects from vibration, tools need to have anti-vibration handles and be in good mechanical condition. The use of gloves to maintain hand temperature and to prevent entry of moisture, together with frequent rest periods and job rotation are suitable controls. The practice of applying sideways force and body weight to breakers to loosen material should be positively discouraged. Health surveillance is recommended where there is regular exposure to vibration exceeding the recommended action level.

Inspection and reporting

92   Excavation and shoring should be inspected by a competent person (ie someone with sufficient training and experience of excavation work) at the start of every shift, after any significant modification to the support system or fall of material, and following any event likely to have affected ground stability. A written report should be made after each seven-day period, unless there has been a collapse/fall

of material or other event likely to affect stability, in which case an inspection and report are required before work continues. A sample form is provided in Appendix 1. The report should contain the following:

(a)   name and address of person on whose behalf the inspection was carried out;
(b)   location of the workplace;
(c)   description of the workplace;
(d)   date and time of inspection;
(e)   details of any factor identified that could pose a health and safety risk;
(f)   details of any action taken;
(g)   details of further action considered necessary;
(h)   name and position of person making the report.

PLANNING, DESIGN AND MANAGEMENT

Risk avoidance and reduction

93   The guiding principle of modern health and safety requirements is that risks to the health and safety of those affected by work activities should be reduced at the outset of planning and design for any project. In other words, consider known hazards from the beginning so that informed planning can take place and design decisions can take account of health and safety risks. In this way it is possible to get rid of risks completely, or at least to reduce them. This should always be considered first before attempting to control risks which need not be there in the first place.

94   There are a number of hazards created by excavation work which include:

(a)   people being trapped or struck by collapse of the side(s);

(b)   people, materials or plant falling into the excavation;

(c)   drowning by flooding of the excavation;

(d)   asphyxiation caused by contamination;

(e)   burns and electric shock caused by damaging existing services.

95   Some of these hazards could be removed by the use of different techniques which avoid the need for excavation, eg using short bored piles for shallow foundations, or tunnelling for the installation of new sewers.

96   Each technique will have its own range of hazards. Substitution of one method for another may result in different risks, and a judgement needs to be made as to which has the greatest potential to cause harm. Where risk remains, the contractor will have to develop methods of managing the risks.

Obtaining information

97   When the pre-tender health and safety plan is developed, it should include relevant information provided by clients[1,37] and other relevant parties relating to the previous use of the site. This is essential where ground contamination could present health risks to workers. Clients should also seek information from utility companies and possibly from previous owners about the existence and location of any underground services so that these may be identified and located before being diverted or cut off. Information should also be sought as to the presence of holes such as shafts, mines and old basements.

Planning, design and management

98   Information from site investigations may also provide a useful indication of the conditions likely to be encountered when excavation commences and the method of support necessary. Such information should be passed to the planning supervisor for inclusion in the pre-tender health and safety plan.

Site investigation

99   A designer, when designing the foundations for a structure should have sufficient knowledge of the engineering properties of the ground on which the structure will be founded. Similarly, designers or specifiers of excavation support also need such information. Site investigation is therefore always necessary for any such structure, though not necessarily for drainage or other service installation work.

100   Site investigation can vary from an examination of the surface deposits using shallow trial pits to a detailed study of the soil, rock and groundwater conditions at depth by the sinking of boreholes. Soil investigations for larger structures with significant foundation loading will normally comprise trial pits or bore holes, *in situ* and laboratory testing and a detailed study of the groundwater conditions. Such site investigations should be carried out under the supervision of competent geotechnical engineers with relevant experience. Where site investigation work is being carried out in ground previously used for industrial purposes, consider the ground as contaminated *until proved otherwise*. Workers should, as a minimum, wear disposable overalls and gloves when working in trial pits or with samples.

101   Those undertaking site investigation need to ensure that enquiries have been made about the presence of underground services before commencing work. The precautions described in paragraphs 51-54 should be taken.

Designing for health and safety

102   The designer should consider how to minimise risks which could arise from excavation work.[38-40] Deep excavation of trenches for drainage can often be avoided by the use of a back-drop manhole, rather than by installing a deep gravity drainage system across a whole site close to the invert level of an existing deep sewer.

> *Faced with the prospect of a 6 m deep drain run across a greenfield site, a designer altered his original design to include a back-drop manhole at the outfall end of the system. This reduced the average trench to a depth of 2.4 m.*

103   The following factors should be taken into account at the design stage:

(a)   previous uses of the site;

(b)   location of existing buildings and services on and adjacent to the site;

(c)   location of the new structures;

(d)   the amount of storage and working space necessary for the excavation and for the construction of the structures;

(e)   the type of soils and their characteristics, taken from the soil investigation;

(f)   the level of the water table and the permeability of the soil;

(g)   ground contamination;

(h)   how much of the excavated material can be reused and the means of disposal of the remainder;

(i)   a suitable scheme for the temporary support of the excavation and for preventing falls into the excavation.

104   Designers can consider using the permanent works to provide support to the excavation and installing that support from ground level, for example the use of diaphragm walls to provide the outer walls of a basement. As well as the need for potentially extensive support works, there may be implications for the timing or sequencing of work. Could the same goal be achieved in another way? Would piling remove the need for deep concrete footings?

> *A client required a new office building with underground parking on a site adjacent to an existing highway. As there was limited space available the designer specified contiguous bored piles for the external walls of the underground car park. This provided permanent support to the highway and support to the sides of the excavation for the car park.*

105   Advances in the design of equipment and guidance systems allow services to be installed in the ground without the need, in some cases, for any excavation. Designers should give careful consideration to the use of such methods as a way to minimise the risks which would otherwise arise from excavation work, see paragraphs 9-10 on trenchless technology.

106   Designers should pass on to contractors all relevant information available to them from site investigation, including both factual information and interpretative reports.

A designer's decision to use a product to prevent clay heave was included in a pre-tender health and safety plan. This enabled contractors to allocate resources for an appropriate shoring method and outline their proposed safe system of work. Tenders were then assessed on the same basis.

107   Consideration needs to be given to:

(a)   designing the scheme to serve the function of both temporary and permanent support, such as contiguous bored piles for retaining walls;

(b)   the location of a building within a plot. This can markedly affect the ability of contractors to maintain safe vehicle routes alongside excavations or to implement control measures with special requirements, such as battering of a slope prior to the construction of a retaining wall in front of it;

(c)   the position of excavations in relation to the route of buried services and overhead lines;

(d)   where risk cannot be eliminated, what information on remaining risks should be passed to the planning supervisor for inclusion in the pre-tender health and safety plan.

A soil investigation revealed large areas of buried contamination. As a result, the designer chose to use a method of driven piling for foundations to avoid bringing contaminated soil to the surface.

108   Information should be provided in the pre-tender health and safety plan on existing site conditions and the availability of service connections so that principal contractors can arrange to have operational welfare facilities as soon as work starts. Planning supervisors are often in the best position to apply at an early stage to utility companies for connection, given the likely delay before connection is made. Sufficient toilet, washing and rest facilities are essential during the groundwork phase of the work, particularly where health risks can be anticipated (see paragraphs 79-86).

For a scheme to construct an office building over 18 months, the planning supervisor applied to utility companies for service connections at the same time as planning permission was being sought. This ensured fully operational welfare facilities from the outset of work at the site.

Risk assessment and method statement

109   A risk assessment[41,42] should be made by the contractor undertaking the work
       before work begins to identify those hazards that are likely to be encountered
       and determine the control measures required. The significant findings of an
       assessment made by an employer of more than five people should be recorded,
       eg in a method statement. Method statements should describe the plant and
       equipment and the safe methods of working required to control the risks
       generated. Method statements should be relevant to the work in hand and easily
       understandable by those who need to use them. They should be proportionate to
       the level of risk and degree of complexity - if the risks and necessary precautions
       are straightforward, short, simple method statements are all that are needed to
       convey the necessary information. The documents should identify the hazards
       associated with the work and any factors which increase the risk of injury, such as:

       (a)   the nature of the ground and groundwater regime;
       (b)   the depth of excavation;
       (c)   the nature of the work required to be undertaken within an excavation;
       (d)   the location of the work, eg readily accessible public place, contaminated
              ground or heavily serviced urban area.

110   A comprehensive list of factors affecting ground movement is given in paragraphs
       11-15.

> *Excavations had been constructed to 2 m deep for mass concrete
> foundations. Normally no one needed to enter these excavations which were
> consequently not supported but a decision to use a product to prevent clay
> heave resulted in a change to the method of work. A groundworker was
> struck and injured by falling material when he entered an unsupported
> trench to fix the product which would otherwise have moved when the
> concrete was poured.*

111   The method of support selected needs to take account of the work to be done
       and allow for adequate working space. It may be necessary to install support in
       relatively shallow excavations of less than 1.2 m deep if ground conditions are
       particularly poor or the nature of the work requires workers to lie or crouch in a
       trench. The options for the method of support may also be limited by ground
       conditions or the presence of services crossing the trench line. Support will also
       be required when plant for excavating or depositing backfill will cause a
       surcharge (see paragraphs 16-17) on the excavation side.

> *A welder drowned at the bottom of a 900 mm deep excavation in poor ground. He had been lying in the trench welding the underside of a steel pipe when a fall of material forced his head into standing water.*

112   Whatever the support method selected, an essential part of the method statement is a defined safe method of work. No person should ever enter an unsupported excavation to install or remove supports. The use of proprietary support systems which can be installed safely from existing ground level may help in this situation. This matter is discussed further in paragraphs 33-42.

> *A worker suffered a broken wrist when part of an excavation side wall fell onto him. He had entered a 1.5 m deep manhole excavation to install timber shoring.*

113   Methods of work need to take into account the following factors to avoid risk of workers being struck by the plant itself or of the materials being placed where visibility is restricted for the plant operator:

(a)   removal from site of surplus excavated material;

(b)   stockpiling of excavated material which is to be reused;

(c)   storage space for materials and working space for workers and plant;

(d)   the type of compaction equipment to be used.

> *A dumper was being used to tip backfill into a trench while a groundworker remained in the trench. A timber baulk had been laid close to the excavation edge to form a stop block. As the dumper approached the excavation it struck the stop block which fell onto the groundworker. The system of work was unsafe due to the position of the groundworker and the unsecured stop block.*

> *A labourer was decapitated by the bucket of a 360° excavator when he went into a trench without the knowledge of the machine operator. The excavator operator did not have a clear view of the trench and no one was acting as banksman.*

114   The method statement should contain the information about the necessary emergency arrangements should an incident occur, unless they are already detailed in the health and safety plan. Details regarding any site-based personnel trained to administer first aid,[43] and the location of the nearest hospital with accident and emergency facilities, should be included. A method for swift communication should be identified and, if there is no telephone available on site, details given on the location of a public telephone close by; otherwise a mobile telephone should be provided. Thought should be given to the actions to be taken if a person were to be injured within a trench or if any gas monitors in use identify the presence of harmful gas or of oxygen deficiency. Employees should be instructed as to all relevant procedures.

115   Consider the additional risks arising to members of the public,[6] in particular to children, those with impaired mobility and the visually impaired. Work should be planned to ensure that excavations are either securely fenced, covered or backfilled overnight and at weekends. Plant should be left in a secure compound and the engines isolated. Stored materials should be stacked carefully to prevent displacement and fenced where otherwise accessible. The risk assessment should determine the precautions necessary to prevent unauthorised access to any construction site. Arrangements for traffic management should also be considered.[7]

> *Two children suffered injury when a crawler crane they managed to start overturned. The crane had been left at a greenfield site over a weekend without precautions to isolate or secure it.*

> *An eight-year-old boy was killed when he was carried over and crushed by the 900 mm diameter concrete pipe he was rolling with a friend. The pipe section had been left adjacent to a public footpath over a weekend without any precautions to prevent tampering.*

Selection of plant

116   All equipment required, including plant for excavating, lifting materials, compaction of backfill, support systems and edge protection should be detailed in the method statement. The equipment and materials identified as being necessary for ground support should be taken to the site so that they are available at the start of excavation work. It is important that the lifting capacity of the plant selected is

checked against maximum lift required. Trench box combinations are by construction very heavy. In addition, friction and suction in certain types of ground can significantly add to the weight of a drag or trench box, and should be taken into account when selecting the size of excavator required to lift it or to move it along the trench.

Lighting

117   Every part of the site which is in use should be sufficiently lit, including approach and traffic routes. This should be, as far as possible, by natural light.

118   Where work will take place beyond daylight hours, artificial lighting should be provided. This is particularly important where plant is in operation. Consideration should also be given to the need for lighting at work sites where there is an interface with members of the public. This may be required after construction work ceases for the day.

119   For further information, see *Lighting at work*.[44]

Management of work

120   Work should not commence until a risk assessment [41,42] has been made and a method statement agreed. Such documents need not be lengthy and can usefully be supplemented by simple drawings. An effective method statement can be one of the best ways to ensure that hazards and control measures are identified, those doing the work are properly instructed, and that the work is effectively supervised.

An inexperienced employee of just 3 weeks, apparently unaware of the risk, was crushed and subsequently died following collapse of clay from the side of a 4 m deep excavation. Trench boxes had been used to support the excavation sides for the full depth but a 1.5 m gap had been left between adjacent boxes. Drainage pipe had already been laid through the unsupported area but the employee entered the excavation via the backfill slope, which provided easy access, to help remove spoil which had fallen over the pipe.

121   Supervisory staff need to ensure that those involved with the work are aware of the hazards and that they are sufficiently trained and experienced to be able to perform the work without endangering themselves or others. The method

statement should be explained to workers and they should have the opportunity to ask for further information about the work. It is a specific requirement of the CHSW Regulations[2] that the installation, dismantling or alteration of any ground support is done only under the supervision of a competent individual who has sufficient experience and training.

122   As work proceeds, supervisors need to check regularly to see that the method statement is followed and that specified precautions are taken. Where site conditions are such that modification of the planned method of work is needed, any changes should be made only after consultation with the person who produced the method statement. A copy of the method statement should be kept on site.

123   On multi-contractor sites, the contractor with overall control should ensure effective co-ordination of overlapping activities; for example excavation beneath scaffolding in use by others could cause instability and collapse of the scaffolding. Sequencing of operations to prevent such overlap is a key requirement and needs to be considered by those designing, planning and undertaking excavation work.

124   The principal contractor's site representatives should make full use of subcontractors' method statements to monitor the work and to ensure that satisfactory health and safety standards are being maintained.

LEGAL REQUIREMENTS

Health and Safety at Work etc Act 1974

125   The principal act covering the health and safety of work people is the Health and Safety at Work etc Act 1974. This places general duties on employers and individuals to manage health and safety to prevent risks to employees, the self-employed and members of the public, see *A guide to the Health and Safety at Work etc Act 1974*.[45]

Management of Health and Safety at Work Regulations 1992

126   Guidance on these Regulations can be found in the publications *Management of Health and Safety at Work Regulations 1992: Approved code of practice*[42] and *5 steps to risk assessment*.[41]

Control of Substances Hazardous to Health Regulations 1994

127   These Regulations require assessment of exposure to hazardous substances and implementation of control measures to reduce the risk of damage to health. Extensive guidance is available.[4,15]

Construction (Design and Management) Regulations 1994

128   These Regulations place duties not only on contractors but also on clients, designers and planning supervisors. Guidance on these Regulations is provided in a number of HSC, HSE and CIRIA publications.[1,37-40]

Construction (Health, Safety and Welfare) Regulations 1996

129   These Regulations place duties on employers, the self-employed and anyone else who controls the way in which any construction work is carried out by those at work. Guidance on these Regulations is provided in the HSE publication *Health and safety in construction*.[46]

FURTHER INFORMATION

APPENDIX 1: SAMPLE INSPECTION REPORT

1   It is not mandatory to use this particular form, but it is mandatory for the inspection to be carried out and recorded in the form of a report, which must be kept available for inspection at all reasonable times by any inspector.

Construction (Health, Safety and Welfare) Regulations 1996

INSPECTION REPORT

Report of results of every inspection made in pursuance of regulation 29(1)

1.   Name and address of person for whom inspection was carried out.

2.   Site address

3.   Date and time of inspection.

4.   Location and description of workplace (including any plant, equipment or materials) inspected.

5.   Matters which give rise to any health and safety risks.

6.   Can work be carried out safely?

Y / N

7.   If not, name of person informed.

8.   Details of any other action taken as a result of matters identified in 5 above.

9.   Details of any further action considered necessary.

10.   Name and position of person making the report.

11.   Date report handed over.

Further information

Construction (Health, Safety and Welfare) Regulations 1996

INSPECTION REPORTS: NOTES

Place of work requiring inspection	Timing and frequency of inspection					
	Before being used for the first time.	After substantial addition, dismantling or alteration.	After any event likely to have affected its strength or stability.	At regular intervals not exceeding 7 days.	Before work at the start of every shift	After accidental fall of rock, earth or any material.
Any working platform or part thereof or any personal suspension equipment.	✓	✓	✓	✓		
Excavations which are supported in pursuit of paragraphs (1), (2) or (3) of regulation 12.			✓		✓	✓
Cofferdams and caissons.			✓		✓	

NOTES

General

1. The inspection report should be completed before the end of the relevant working period.
2. The person who prepares the report should, within 24 hours, provide either the report or a copy to the person on whose behalf the inspection was carried out.
3. The report should be kept on site until work is complete. It should then be retained for three months at an office of the person for whom the inspection was carried out.

Working platforms only

1. An inspection is only required where a person is liable to fall more than 2 metres from a place of work.
2. Any employer or any other person who controls the activities of persons using a scaffold shall ensure that it is stable and of sound construction and that the relevant safeguards are in place before his employees or persons under his control first use the scaffold.
3. No report is required following the inspection of any mobile tower scaffold which remains in the same place for less than 7 days.
4. Where an inspection of a working platform or part thereof or any personal suspension equipment is carried out:
   i.   before it is taken into use for the first time; or
   ii. after any substantial addition, dismantling or other alteration;
   not more than one report is required for any 24 hour period.

Excavations only

1. The duties to inspect and prepare a report apply only to any excavation which needs to be supported to prevent any person being trapped or buried by an accidental collapse, fall or dislodgement of material from its sides, roof or area adjacent to it. Although an excavation must be inspected at the start of every shift, only one report of such inspections is required every 7 days. Reports must be completed for all inspections carried out during this period for other purposes, e.g. after accidental fall of material.

Checklist of typical scaffolding faults

Footings	Standards	Ledgers	Bracing	Putlogs and transoms	Couplings	Bridles	Ties	Boarding	Guard-rails and toe-boards	Ladders
Soft and uneven	Not plumb	Not level	Some missing	Wrongly spaced	Wrong fitting	Wrong spacing	Some missing	Bad boards	Wrong height	Damaged
No base plates	Jointed at same height	Joints in same bay	Loose	Loose	Loose	Wrong couplings	Loose	Trap boards	Loose	Insufficient length
No sole plates	Wrong spacing	Loose	Wrong fittings	Wrongly supported	Damaged	No check couplers	Not enough	Incomplete	Some missing	Not tied
Undermined	Damaged	Damaged	-	-	No check couplers	-	-	Insufficient supports	-	-

REFERENCES AND FURTHER READING

References

1   *Managing construction for health and safety - Construction (Design and Management) Regulations 1994. Approved Code of Practice* L54 HSE Books 1995 ISBN 0 7176 0792 5

2   *Construction (Health, Safety and Welfare) Regulations 1996* SI 1996/1592 HSE Books 1996 ISBN 0 11 035904 6

3   *Avoiding danger from underground services* HSG47 HSE Books 1989 ISBN 0 7176 0435 7 (Currently being revised)

4   *General COSHH ACOP - Control of Substances Hazardous to Health Regulations 1994. Approved Code of Practice* L5 HSE Books 1997 ISBN 0 7176 1308 9

5   *Avoidance of danger from overhead electric lines* GS6(rev) HSE Books 1991 ISBN 0 11 885668 5

6   *Protecting the public - your next move* HSG151 HSE Books 1997 ISBN 0 7176 1148 5

7   *Safety at street works and road works. Code of practice* HMSO 1992 ISBN 0 11 551144 X

8   *Safe use of ladders, step ladders and trestles* GS31 HSE Books 1984 ISBN 0 176 1023 3

9   *Workplace transport safety - guidance for employers* HSG136 HSE Books 1995 ISBN 0 7176 0935 9

10   *Manual handling - Manual Handling Operations Regulations 1992. Approved Code of Practice and guidance* L23 HSE Books 1992 ISBN 0 7176 0411 X

11   *Getting to grips with manual handling - a short guide for employers* INDG143 HSE Books 1993

12   *Manual handling: Solutions you can handle* HSG115 HSE Books 1994 ISBN 0 7176 0693 7

13   *Safe work in confined spaces. Approved Code of Practice, Regulations and guidance* L101 HSE Books 1997 ISBN 0 7176 1405 0

14   *Protection of workers and the general public during the development of contaminated land*
HSG66 HSE Books 1991 ISBN 0 11 885657 X (Currently being revised)

15   *A step-by-step guide to COSHH assessments* COSHH HSG97 HSE Books 1993
ISBN 0 11 886379 7

16   *Health risk management* HSG137 HSE Books 1995 ISBN 0 7176 0905 7

17   *Leptospirosis* INDG184 HSE Books 1990

18   *Working with sewage: The health hazards - A guide for employers* INDG198
HSE Books 1995

19   *Working with sewage: The health hazards - A guide for employees* INDG197
HSE Books 1995

20   *Special Waste Regulations 1996: How they affect you* WP147 (available in England and
Wales from local Environment Agency offices and in Scotland from local Scottish
Environment Protection Agency offices)

Personal protective equipment CIS28-35

21   No 28 *PPE: Principles, duties and responsibilities* HSE Books 1993

22   No 29 *PPE: Head protection* HSE Books 1993

23   No 30 *PPE: Hearing protection* HSE Books 1993

24   No 31 *PPE: Eye and face protection* HSE Books 1993

25   No 32 *PPE: Respiratory protective equipment* HSE Books 1993

26   No 33 *PPE: General and specialist clothing* HSE Books 1993

27   No 34 *PPE: Gloves* HSE Books 1993

28   No 35 *PPE: Safety footwear* HSE Books 1993

29   *Provision of welfare facilities at transient construction sites* CIS46 HSE Books 1997

30   *Provision of welfare facilities at fixed construction sites* CIS18 HSE Books 1996

31   *Dust and noise in the construction process* CRR 73 HSE Books 1995
ISBN 0 7176 0768 2

32   *Introducing the Noise at Work Regulations* INDG75 HSE Books 1996

33   *Noise in construction* INDG127 HSE Books 1993

34   *Reducing noise at work - Guidance on the Noise at Work Regulations 1989* L108
HSE Books 1989 ISBN 0 7176 0454 3

35   *Hand-arm vibration* HSG88 HSE Books 1994 ISBN 0 7176 1511 1

36   *Vibration solutions - Practical ways to reduce hand-arm vibration injury*
HSG170 HSE BOOKS 1997 ISBN 0 7176 0954 5

37   *A guide to managing health and safety in construction* HSE Books 1995
ISBN 0 7176 0755 0

38   *Information on site safety for designers of smaller building projects* CRR 72 HSE Books
1995 ISBN 0 7176 0777 1

39   *Designing for health and safety in construction* HSE Books 1995
ISBN 0 7176 0807 7

40   *CDM Regulations - Work sector guidance for designers* CIRIA Report 166 *Construction
Industry Research and Information Association* 1997 ISBN 0 86017 464 6

41   *5 steps to risk assessment* INDG163 HSE Books 1994

42   *Management of Health and Safety at Work Regulations 1992. Approved Code of Practice*
L21 HSE Books 1992 ISBN 0 7176 0412 8

43   *First aid at work - Health and Safety (First Aid) Regulations 1981. Approved Code of
Practice and guidance* L74 HSE Books 1997 ISBN 0 7176 1050 0

44   *Lighting at work* HSG38 HSE Books 1997 ISBN 0 7176 1232 5

45   *A guide to the Health and Safety at Work etc Act 1974 - Guidance on the Act*
L1 HSE Books 1992 ISBN 0 7176 0441 1

46   *Health and safety in construction* HSG150 HSE Books 1996 ISBN 0 7176 1143 4

General information

HSC Newsletter - published six times a year and is available by subscription only. Subscription enquiries should be made to HSE Books Subscriptions Department, HSE Books, PO Box 1999, Sudbury, Suffolk CO10 6FS (Tel: 01787 881165)

Site Safe News - published twice a year. If you would like to receive free copies regularly, write to Sir Robert Jones Memorial Workshops, Units 3 and 5-9, Grain Industrial Estate, Harlow Street, Liverpool L8 4XY (Tel: 0151 709 1354/5/6)

Selecting a health and safety consultancy INDG133 HSE Books 1992

The future availability and accuracy of the references listed in this publication cannot be guaranteed.

GLOSSARY

Angle of repose The angle measured in degrees to the horizontal which ground material, if left, will ultimately form to become completely stable.

Batter A uniform steep slope to an excavation to reduce the risk of the side(s) collapsing, expressed as one horizontal linear unit to a number of vertical linear units.

Close sheeting Vertical or horizontal *sheeting* placed close together to hold up the ground in an excavation.

Cross poling *Poling boards* placed horizontally in trenching operations across a gap between *runners* or *sheeting* and tucked in behind them and used where *runners or sheeting* cannot be driven continuously and vertically.

Deep well system Local lowering of the level of the groundwater in deep excavations in which individual submersible pumps are installed in holes bored to the required depth.

Design brief Instructions given to designers on the requirements of the structure or building.

Ground freezing Method of temporarily stabilising ground by local freezing of the water within it.

Open sheeting *Sheeting* spaced at intervals in an excavation, to support ground that is sufficiently firm to make *close sheeting* unnecessary.

Permanent works The construction work undertaken to form the final building or structure.

Poling board Sheeting, usually 1 m to 5 m long, in contact with the ground and supporting the face or the sides of an excavation.

Props Timber, tubular steel or adjustable steel screw supports which span from one side of an excavation to the opposite side, often between a pair of *trench sheets* and which are subjected to compressive load.

Puncheon Post to support a higher *waling* or strut from the one below.

Raking shore Inclined prop or support.

Runner Vertical member used to support the sides or face of an excavation and progressively driven as excavation proceeds, its lower end being kept below the bottom of the excavation.

Sheeting Steel sheets or timber boards used to support the ground in an excavation.

Soil stabilisation The injection of cementitious materials including cement, bentonite, pulverised fly ash, or chemical mixtures to enhance the strength of the ground or to reduce its permeability.

Steel sheet pile Interlocking or clutched profiled steel sections designed for driving into the ground to resist lateral pressure.

Struts See explanation of props.

Surcharge Vertical loading imposed on the ground which increases the horizontal load in the ground and hence the active force on the earthworks support.

Temporary works Work undertaken to enable other construction work to take place which is later removed and does not form part of the final building or structure.

Toeing-in The process of driving *trench sheets* or *runners* into the ground at the base of an excavation to provide lateral support.

Trench sheets Long narrow thin sections, usually of cold rolled steel plate formed to lap-joint or interlock at it edges with adjacent sheets, generally installed vertically to support the sides of trenches and excavations.

Underpinning Introduction of support under an existing structure.

Waling A horizontal beam that supports *sheeting* against pressure.

Water table The natural level of water within the ground.

Well point Small diameter, usually about 50 mm diameter, long tube installed vertically in the ground to the required depth, that has a perforated length near the foot, through which groundwater is pumped.

Well pointing The installation of boreholes and pumps in the vicinity of an excavation to locally depress the level of the water table.

Well point system Local lowering of the level of the groundwater by pumping through a number of well points usually located around the periphery of an excavation.

C150   2/99

Printed and published by the Health and Safety Executive
C150   2/99

Further information